Pin it on

Speed Sounds

Consonants   *Ask children to say the sounds.*

f	l	m	n	r	s	v	z	sh	**th**	ng
										nk

b	c	d	g	h	j	p	qu	t	w	x	y	**ch**
	k											

Vowels   *Ask children to say the sounds in and out of order.*

a	e	i	o	u

Each box contains one sound but sometimes more than one grapheme.
*Focus graphemes for this story are **circled**.*

Ditty 1   Pin it on

Story Green Words

Ask children to read the words first in Fred Talk and then say the word.

pin	on	not	leg
chin	tum	yes	

Ask children to read the root first and then the whole word with the ending.

that → that's

Pin it on

In this story, some children are playing a game called 'Pin the tail on the donkey'. They are blindfolded, and need to attach the tail to the right place. Let's see how they do!

pin it on

not on its leg

4

not on its chin

not on its tum

yes

that's it

pin it on

Ditty 2 Let's run

Story Green Words

Ask children to read the words first in Fred Talk and then say the word.

zip   up   run

Ask children to read the root first and then the whole word with the ending.

let → let's

Red Words

Ask children to practise reading the word.

put

Let's run

Introduction

Do you like snow? It can be exciting when it snows, but you need to be wearing the right clothes when you go out!

put it on

zip it up

put it on

put them on

let's run

Ditty 3 A fun hat

Story Green Words

Ask children to read the words first in Fred Talk and then say the word.

hen	in	red	hat
fox	sun	man	top
kid	fun		

A fun hat

Do you have any hats? In this story, we see lots of special hats...

a hen in a red hat

a fox in a sun hat

a man in a top hat

a kid in a fun hat

Questions to talk about

Read out each question and ask children to TTYP (turn to your partner) and discuss.

Ditty 1

Where does the first girl pin the tail?

Do the children like playing the game?

What sort of games do you like to play at parties?

Ditty 2

What is the second thing that the boy puts on?

What do Mum and the boy do in the snow?

What do you put on when you go out in the snow?

Ditty 3

What type of hat does the fox have?

Which hat is your favourite?

How many other sorts of hats can you think of?

Speedy Green Words

Ask children to practise reading the words across the rows, down the columns and in and out of order clearly and quickly.

it	on	a	on
a	it	on	it